HiT entertainment

Panini BOOKS

Art Attack Annual 2009 is published under licence by Panini Publishing, a division of Panini UK Limited. Office of publication: Brockbourne House, 77 Mount Ephraim, Tunbridge Wells, Kent TN4 8BS. This publication may not be sold, except by authorised dealers, and is sold subject to the condition that it shall not be sold or distributed with any part of its cover or markings removed, nor in a mutilated condition. Printed in Italy. ISBN: 1-904419-98-4

W9-DJH-807

£6.99

LET'S HAVE AN ART ATTACK!

Welcome to the Art Attack Annual 2009!

Inside, there are tons of things to make and do, and you don't need to be a brilliant artist to create something impressive! So don't throw away all your household rubbish – save it up and turn it into something wonderful!

Neil Buchanan

WHAT'S INSIDE...

MAKE IT SNAPPY!

THIS HUNGRY ALLIGATOR IS JUST WAITING TO GOBBLE YOUR GARBAGE – JUST WATCH OUT FOR THOSE TEETH!

1 Cut two feet from cardboard and tape them to the base of the bucket.

2 Copy the shape here and cut out a cardboard head with teeth. Lightly score along the dotted line, so the teeth can be bent into position. You will need to ask an adult to help you.

3 Tape the head in place. The wide end should cover about half of the rim of the bucket.

4 Bend the nose over and tape the ends together. Bend the teeth into place. Cut another row of teeth and stick them around the rim of the bucket. Wedge the cardboard tube in position to support the head and tape it on.

5 Make a long, wedge-shaped tail from newspaper and tape it onto the bucket. Add balls of newspaper in rows across the tail and back to look like bumpy skin.

YOU WILL NEED:

A small bucket with the handle removed, cardboard, newspaper, long cardboard tube, PVA glue, paint, paintbrush, green crêpe paper, pink tissue paper.

Cover the body with three layers of papier mâché and the head and front of the bucket with two layers. Leave it to dry.

Finish by covering the whole thing with two layers of papier mâché using green crêpe paper. Add balls of kitchen paper mixed with PVA glue for eyes and paint them white with black pupils. Stick the pink tissue paper to the inside of the mouth.

NOW TOSS IN YOUR RUBBISH! BUT MIND YOUR FINGERS!

To empty your bin, take a deep breath and delve in past those sharp teeth – we dare you!

SPEEDY SPIDERS!

Enjoy the screams as these tearaway terrors speed across the floor

YOU WILL NEED:

Old toy cars, egg boxes, thin card, sticky tape, old newspapers, black tissue paper, PVA glue, paint, googly eyes, clear drinking straw, black pipe cleaners.

1 Tape four black pipe cleaners on to a toy car, bending them into leg shapes. Trim them so they do not touch the ground. Take care not to cover the wheels.

2 Tape a scrunched-up ball of newspaper over the whole car to form the body shape.

3 Cover the whole thing with two layers of papier mâché, using black tissue paper, avoiding the wheels. Leave it to dry, then stick on some googly eyes.

SHIMMERING SHAPES!

ADD SOME SPARKLE TO YOUR LIFE WITH THESE SUPER SHINY GLITTER STICKERS!

YOU WILL NEED:
Paintbrush, PVA glue, glitter, a plastic surface.

1 Find a plastic surface, like an old tray. Check with an adult before you start.

2 Using an old paintbrush and PVA glue, make lots of different shapes. Paint the glue on quite thickly.

3 Sprinkle lots of glitter over the shapes and leave them to dry.

4 Carefully peel the shapes off the surface, then use them to decorate your window or a mirror!

If you fancy a change, simply peel off the stickers and stick them somewhere else!

GIVE US A WAVE!

Construct a simple frame or 'skeleton.' Begin with the head and spine. Add shoulders and hips, then limbs. Flesh out your frame with simple shapes and finally add details such as features and clothes.

RUN FOR IT

If you need to, get someone to pose for you. Take a close look at how their arms and legs look!

SITTING Keep it simple. Even this sitting pose can be easy to draw!

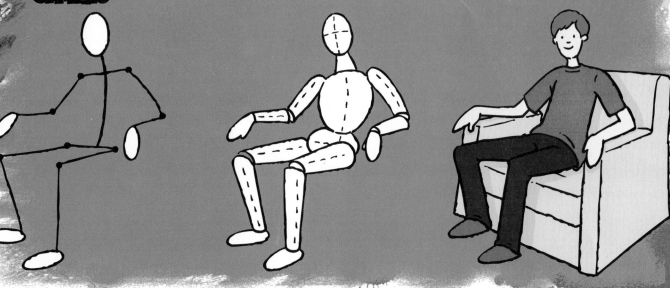

JUMPING You'll be jumping for joy with your new-found drawing skills!

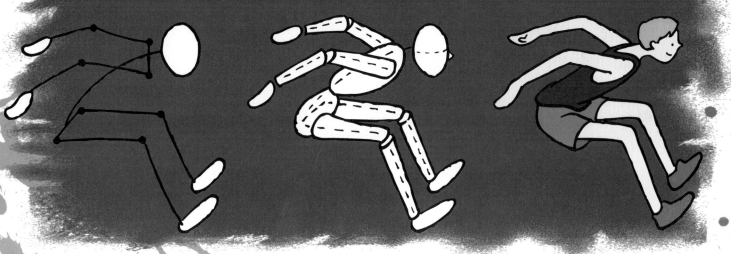

WALKING Try to keep the drawing fluid and relaxed - there's nothing to it!

KNOCK DOWN

AHOY THERE, ME HEARTIES - HAVE A GO AT MAKING THIS COOL PIRATE GAME! STAND THEM ON THEIR TREASURE ISLAND AND THEN KNOCK THEM DOWN!

1 To make a pirate, place a crumpled ball of newspaper on top of an empty plastic bottle and tape it firmly in place. For the arms, use pieces of rolled-up cardboard.

2 You can add details to each pirate, to give it a bit of character and individuality. Make a hat or beard from a scrunched-up piece of newspaper. Cut a sword from a piece of cardboard.

3 Cover each pirate with three or four layers of torn paper pasted on with PVA glue. Leave them to dry until they're rock hard.

PIRATES!

4

Meanwhile, make the base. Glue a long cardboard tube to a rectangle of cardboard box card. Stick one end of a length of string onto a rubber or paper pulp ball and stick the other end into the top of the tube.

YOU WILL NEED:

Plastic bottles, sticky tape, cardboard, newspaper, PVA glue, string, rubber ball, cardboard tube, paints.

13

5 Cover with papier mâché. When dry, paint the base to look like an island in the sea. Use yellow and orange for the island and when that's dry, paint the sea blue. Then add white for frothy waves. Paint the tube and ball.

6 Paint the pirates. Look at the pirates on this page for ideas on how to dress them. Add eye patches and spotty scarves for that authentic sea dog look!

CREATE A WOOLLY JUMPER BY PAINTING LINES AROUND THE NECK, SLEEVES AND BOTTOM.

TRY PAINTING DETAILS SUCH AS BELTS AND A WAISTCOAT.

PAINT A STRIPY T-SHIRT AND THIN MOUSTACHE!

ADD A SKULL AND CROSSBONES AND A SPOTTY SCARF.

Crisp tube, 3 toilet roll tubes, 2 kitchen roll tubes, thick and thin card, safety scissors, sticky tape, paints, paintbrush.

5

Paint your castle as shown, or choose your favourite, fairytale colours!

LEAVE THE ROOFS LOOSE INSTEAD OF TAPING THEM DOWN, SO YOU CAN POP IN YOUR PENS AND PENCILS!

17

TREASURE CHEST

THIS ANCIENT SILVER CHEST IS THE PERFECT PLACE TO STORE ALL YOUR SECRET STUFF AND HIDE YOUR FAVOURITE TREASURES.

1

To make the lid of the treasure chest, cut a piece of cereal box card or cardboard box card to the same length as the shoe box lid and curve it over as shown. Fix it in place with sticky tape.

2

Stand the lid on its end on another piece of card and draw around its semi-circular shape. Cut the shape out, then do the same for the other end. Stick the shapes to the ends with sticky tape.

3

Tape two folded strips of newspaper over the top of the lid to make two raised straps.

4

Cut out a keyhole, eight triangles and two arrows from card and attach them to the box with sticky tape as shown. Dip small balls of kitchen paper into PVA glue mixed with water and stick them to the straps at regular intervals to look like bolts.

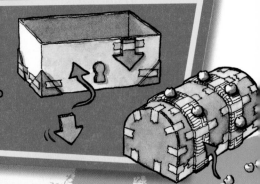

5

Cover the whole box and lid with strips of black tissue paper, brushing the glue mixture on top. Keep the box and lid separate, so they don't stick together. Leave it to dry overnight.

YOU WILL NEED: Shoe box, cereal box card or cardboard box card, newspaper, black tissue paper, kitchen paper, PVA glue, sticky tape, silver paint, safety scissors, stick-on gems.

6

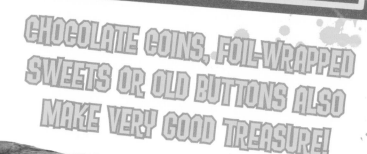

Use a ball of kitchen paper to dab silver paint over the whole box and lid, but don't press the paint into the creases. Leave it to dry. Add some stick-on gems to decorate your box and make it look even more valuable, then fill it with treasure!

PASTA JEWELS

Paint pieces of dried pasta with gold and silver metallic paint, then thread them onto a length of string to make a stunning necklace.

CHOCOLATE COINS, FOIL-WRAPPED SWEETS OR OLD BUTTONS ALSO MAKE VERY GOOD TREASURE!

SILVER GOBLET

YOU WILL NEED: Plastic drinks bottle, card, PVA glue, safety scissors, sticky tape, silver foil, stick-on gems.

1. Ask an adult to help you cut the top third from a plastic drinks bottle, leaving the lid on.
2. Cut a circle of card to make the base of the goblet and tape the card to the top of the bottle with sticky tape.
3. Cover the whole of the goblet inside and out with pieces of silver foil, stuck on with PVA.
4. Add some stick-on gems for extra sparkle.

19

MONSTER MAD!

SCARE YOURSELF SILLY WITH A MONSTER BURSTING THROUGH THE WALL OF YOUR BEDROOM!

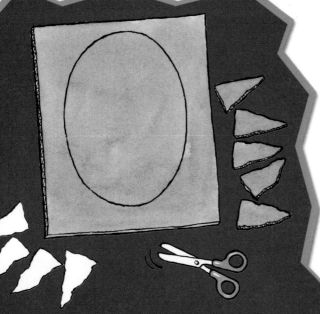

1 Cut out a large oval from a piece of cardboard. Rip some white paper into rough triangle shapes. Do the same with cardboard box card, tearing rough, slightly larger triangles.

2 Glue the cardboard triangles all the way around the card oval, facing inwards. Stick the paper triangles on top of the card ones.

3 When dry, bend the triangles back so it looks like a hole in the wall with torn wallpaper.

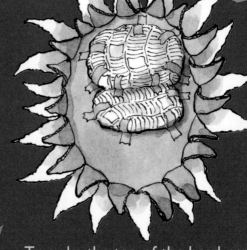

4 To make the top of the head, scrunch up a sheet of newspaper and tape it at the top of the oval. Scrunch up a smaller piece and tape it underneath to make the jaw.

20

5 Roll up a sheet of newspaper into a thin sausage shape and bend it around to form lips. Use balls of paper for eyes, small sausage shapes for eyebrows and triangles of card for teeth.

21

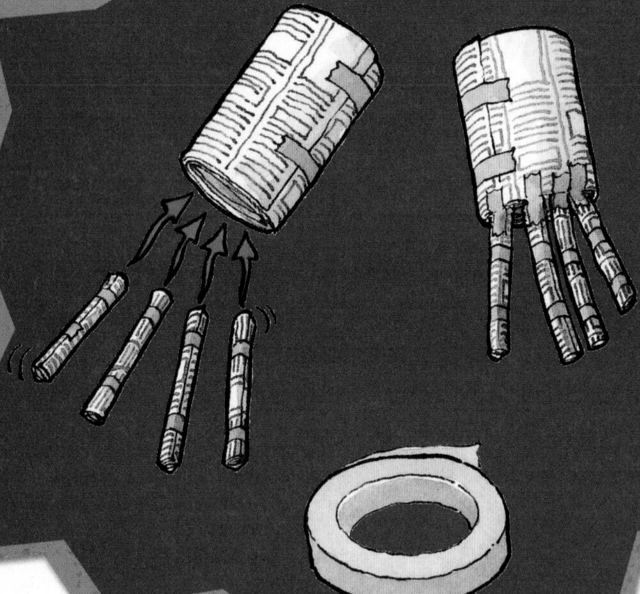

6

For the hands, scrunch up two square-shaped balls of newspaper. Roll up some tubes of newspaper and cut them to size for fingers. Tape these to the hands.

7

Attach the hands under the face. Now cover the whole thing with three layers of torn newspaper pasted on with PVA glue. Leave it to dry.

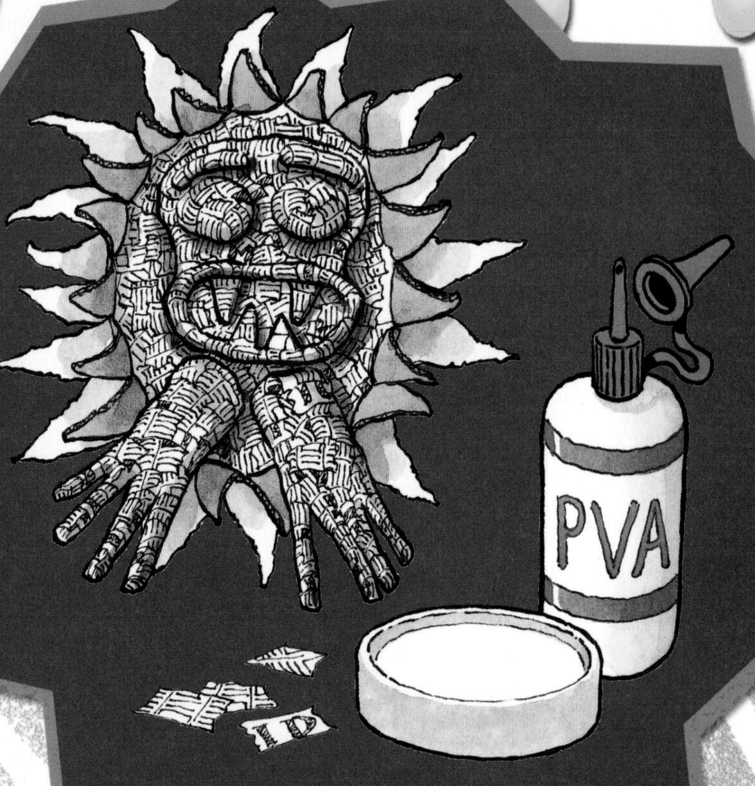

PVA

8

Paint black all the way around your monster to make it look like a hole then paint him green. Paint the mouth red, and eyes and teeth white. When the paint has dried, add details with a black permanent marker.

JUNGLE BEAT

CHEAP WOODEN CHOPSTICKS BOUND WITH STRING AND PAINTED WITH PATTERNS MAKE GREAT DRUMSTICKS!

YOU WILL NEED:

An empty paint tin, safety scissors, coloured corrugated card, sticky tape, black felt, PVA glue, string, wooden chopsticks.

1 Ask an adult to clean out an old paint tin and remove the handle. Put the lid on the tin.

2 Cut a length of corrugated card to fit around the tin at the exact height. Stick the card in place with PVA glue.

3 Cut a square of black felt larger than the circumference of the tin and round off the corners. Stick it over the top of the drum with a small amount of PVA.

4 Wrap string around the top and bottom of the tin, folding the felt down into place. Fix it in place with PVA.

5 Paint tribal designs on the top and sides of the drum.

6 Finish by sticking string in a zig-zag pattern around the edge of the drum. Now it's time to make music!

23

GRRRR-EAT!

YOU WILL NEED:
Safety scissors, thin card, glue, felt-tip pens, 4 paper fasteners.

MAKE YOUR OWN MOVING CIRCUS SCENE!

1 Trace or photocopy the pictures on the opposite page and stick them onto thin card. Colour in all the pieces.

2 Carefully cut out all the pictures, following the dotted lines. Make holes where marked at A, B, C and D.

3 Attach the lion and lion tamer to the background using paper fasteners. Match up the letters to make sure that you are putting the pieces in the right places.

24

FISH HOOKS!

THESE LOVELY FISH ARE SO SIMPLE TO MAKE, YOU'LL SOON BE HOOKED!

Draw and cut out a fish shape from card. Make it as fancy as you like by adding fins and a swirly tail.

TRY MAKING LOTS OF DIFFERENT FISH IN CRAZY COLOURS!

26

YOU WILL NEED:

Cardboard, newspaper, safety scissors, crêpe paper, PVA glue, double-sided sticky pad, hook.

2 Pad out its body with scrunched-up newspaper.

3 Cover the whole shape with papier mâché. Finish with a layer of brightly coloured crêpe paper and leave it to dry.

4 Cut stripes or spots from a contrasting colour crêpe paper and glue them in position.

5 Add red crêpe paper for lips and stick on an eye and eyelashes. To finish, use a double-sided sticky pad to attach a hook to the back of the fish.

YOU COULD FIX YOUR FISH OVER AN EXISTING HOOK IN YOUR ROOM, MAKING SURE YOU LEAVE ROOM TO HANG THINGS UP!

GIVE ME AN "A"!

WHAT DO WE WANT? FUN THINGS TO MAKE!
WHEN DO WE WANT THEM? NOW!

MEGAPHONE

YOU WILL NEED:
Thin card, sticky tape, safety scissors, tissue paper, PVA glue, paints, paintbrush, silver card, stick-on stars, red and white crêpe paper, double-sided tape.

1 Take a rectangle of thin card and roll it into a cone shape. Fix it in position with tape and trim the ends to make a neat cone.

2 Cover the entire shape with a layer of tissue paper and diluted PVA glue, inside and out. I've used red tissue paper, but you can use whatever colour you like!

3 When it's dry, paint on details with silver paint and stick on stars or team logos.

4 Make a small cone of silver card and glue it to the small end of the cone. To make a handle, fold a strip of silver card in half lengthways and glue it in place.

CHOOSE COLOURS TO MATCH THE KIT OF YOUR FAVOURITE TEAM!

POM-POMS

YOU WILL NEED: Thin card, red and white crêpe paper, red tissue paper, silver card, stick-on stars, paint, sticky tape.

1 Make the handles by rolling rectangles of card into thin tubes and securing them with double-sided sticky tape.

2 Cut each roll of crêpe paper in half widthways. Cut each bundle into 2cm strips lengthways, leaving about 3cm uncut at the bottom.

3 Unroll two lengths of cut crêpe paper in different colours. Place one on top of the other, then roll them back up again tightly, so the colours are mixed together.

4 Push the uncut end of the crêpe paper into the card tube handles and secure them with tape. Shake out your pom-poms and you're ready for action!

THINGS TO DO WITH

Create some wrinkly Art Attacks using corrugated paper or card. You can find corrugated card in cardboard boxes or you can buy it from craft shops.

CORRUGATED CASE!

MAKE A COOL FOLDER TO KEEP YOUR ART ATTACK DRAWINGS IN.

Cut two rectangles of corrugated card, one longer than the other, and cut a rounded edge around each piece.

Place the long rectangle on a table with the smaller piece on top. The corrugated sides should be on the outside. Hold them together as you punch holes round the edges and thread with string. Fold the longer bit down to form a flap. Punch two holes in the flap (as illustrated), then glue a length of string in place behind the flap to the front of the folder, make sure there is enough string to thread through the flaps and tie the folder shut.

PENCIL POT!

A UNIQUE CONTAINER FOR YOUR PENS, PENCILS AND PAINT BRUSHES.

Use coloured corrugated card or paper to decorate an empty cardboard snack tube. Stick the ridged paper around the outside and on the inside.

Or you can use plain corrugated card and then paint it. Not only does it give a great-looking texture but the ridges make it easy to bend around the container.

I finished the pot off with a foam flower but you could make decorations from anything you like.

CORRUGATED CARD!

CRINKLE CARDS!

SEND A MESSAGE WITH A CORRUGATED COLLAGE CARD.

Corrugated card or paper is perfect for making collages as well.

Here I've created some fantastic birthday cards! If you don't have any coloured corrugated card, simply get some ordinary ridged card from a cardboard box and paint it.

Sketch out your idea for a greetings card or picture first, then cut out pieces of different coloured card and use paper glue to layer them onto a bigger piece of folded card.

CROWNING GLORY!

CORRUGATED CARD STOPS YOU FROM GOING ROUND THE BEND!

Corrugated card is used in boxes because it is strong but lightweight. Use it to make strong foundations for your papier mâché models.

It's also useful for making curved shapes. Bend corrugated card with the ridges running from top to bottom - perfect for shapes like this crown.

MOONLIGHT MOBILE!

1 Trace or photocopy the page opposite and stick it onto a piece of thin card.

YOU WILL NEED:
Safety scissors, thin card, glue, felt-tip pens, glitter, string.

2 Colour in the pictures and add some glitter for extra sparkle! You could even stick on some sequins if you like.

3 Carefully cut out all the pieces and make a hole on each of the black dots. Ask an adult to help you with this.

4 Thread pieces of string through the holes to join the fairies and stars together, then tie these to the moon. Finally, thread another piece of string through the hole at the top of the moon and make a loop to hang it up.

32

GEISHA GIRL!

JAPANESE GEISHAS WEAR TRADITIONAL KIMONOS - OFTEN ELABORATELY DECORATED. HAVE A GO AT DECORATING THEM YOURSELVES.

Make a small screen tidy or greetings card by tracing off both sides onto folded card. Decorate as you wish. Use 3D paints and gold and silver to create a really elaborate gown.

If you cut the geisha girl out, you can make a book mark. I looked up some Japanese letters and decorated the sleeves with black felt pen.

How to Draw YOUR HOME!

HOME SWEET HOME!

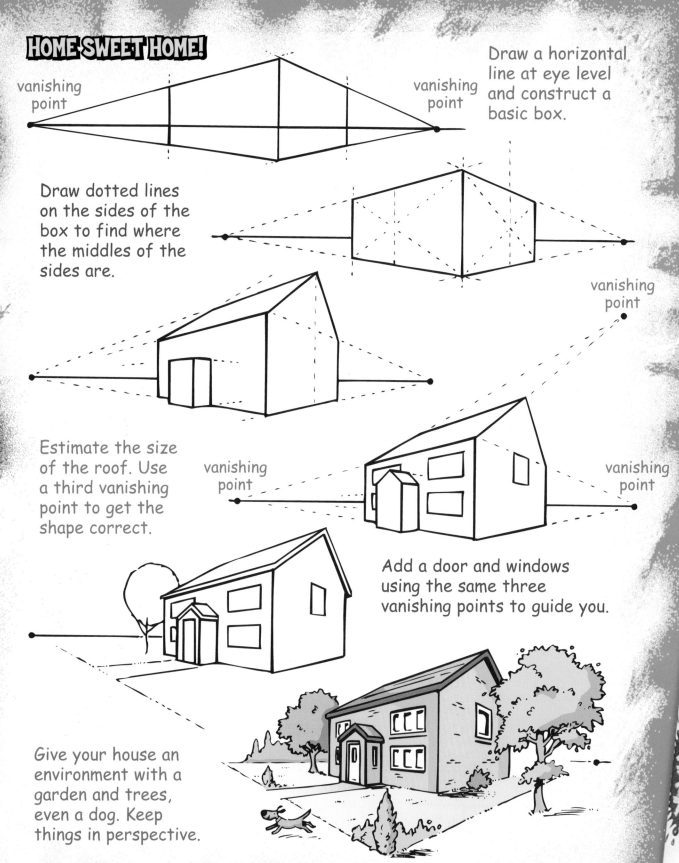

vanishing point

vanishing point

Draw a horizontal line at eye level and construct a basic box.

Draw dotted lines on the sides of the box to find where the middles of the sides are.

vanishing point

Estimate the size of the roof. Use a third vanishing point to get the shape correct.

vanishing point

vanishing point

vanishing point

Add a door and windows using the same three vanishing points to guide you.

Give your house an environment with a garden and trees, even a dog. Keep things in perspective.

ROOM WITH A VIEW! Design a room using the principles of perspective.

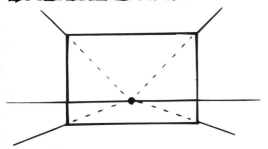

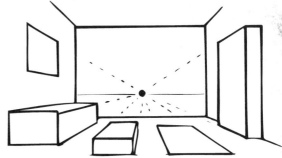

Draw a rectangle with a horizontal line towards the bottom to mark eye level. Add a small dot in the middle as this is your vanishing point.

Using a ruler as a pivot, draw furniture, a rug and pictures. Erase unwanted pencil marks before completing your picture.

BOXED OFF! Sketch a cube shape and then draw a table and a chair.

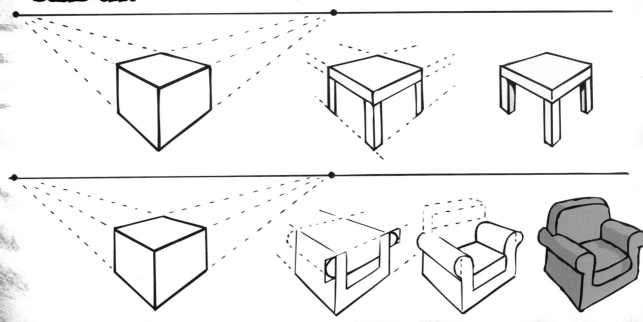

37

ROLL UP, ROLL UP!

This ringmaster will help hold your door open and welcome the audience in!

1 Fill a clean plastic bottle with sand or small pebbles and replace the lid. Cut a piece of card for the ringmaster's feet and glue it to the base of the bottle.

2 Using a mixture of PVA glue and water, paste kitchen paper to the bottom half of the bottle to pad out the ringmaster's legs. Scrunch up some more kitchen paper to give his feet a 3D look.

3 Glue a strip of card around the ringmaster's waist to make his cummerbund. Cut a jacket shape from card as shown and glue this around the bottle, too.

4 Fix pieces of rolled-up kitchen paper on with sticky tape to make the arms and lapels, then cover the whole thing with two layers of papier mâché. Roll up a ball of kitchen paper and tape it on top of the bottle to form his head.

YOU WILL NEED:

2-litre plastic bottle, sand, newspaper, kitchen paper, card, PVA glue, paints, paintbrush, sticky tape.

5

Draw two circles on a piece of card, one inside the other, and cut them out to make the brim. The middle circle is the top of the hat. Wrap a rectangle of card around the circle and fix it on top of the brim with sticky tape. Put this on the ringmaster's head and cover it with a layer of papier mâché.

6

When the papier mâché is dry, paint the ringmaster. The traditional colours for his outfit are black and red, as shown here, but you could paint it any colour you like!

PARTY TIME!

YOU WILL NEED:
Potato, craft foam, string, elastic band, coloured card, paint.

CREATE YOUR OWN PERSONALISED PARTY INVITATIONS!

Use the edge of a piece of craft foam to print the words. Bend it round to make the curved letters.

Cut balloon shapes from craft foam and use the edge of a long piece of craft foam to print the strings.

Cut a horse shape from card and print it in brown paint. Use string dipped in darker brown paint to print his tail and mane.

To make the acrobat, ask an adult to help you cut a potato in half and carve out the different shapes. Dip each piece in some paint and press it onto the paper, then add the details with a fine paintbrush or a marker pen.

The zigzag pattern at the top and bottom are printed with a short piece of elastic band. Glue it to the end of a piece of card to use as a handle. Use your fingertip to print the dots.

HOW ABOUT MAKING UP SOME DIFFERENT DESIGNS? YOU COULD PRINT A CLOWN'S FACE OR SOME CIRCUS AMIMALS!

40

QUICK CRABS!

THESE CUTE CRABS
LOOK BRILLIANT AND
ARE EASY TO MAKE!

YOU WILL NEED:

Coloured
corrugated card,
coloured card,
scissors,
pipe cleaners,
googly eyes.

1 Cut oval shapes from coloured corrugated card. Stick these on plain card in a contrasting colour and cut out again.

2 Cut small rectangles of card, fold in half and use them to stick two ovals together like a hinge.

3 Stick pieces of corrugated card back to back, and cut out pairs of claws using the claw template. Stick these inside the shell, at either side.

4 Make legs from strips of paper or pipe cleaners. Stick these either side of the shell as well.

5 Close and secure the shell and stick on some googly eyes at the front.

41

COLOURFUL CLOWN!

PHOTOCOPY OR TRACE THE CLOWN PICTURE TO HAVE AN ART ATTACK!

DECORATE THE CLOWN ANY WAY YOU WISH!
I PAINTED MY CLOWN AND WHEN IT WAS DRY,
I EDGED EVERYTHING WITH BLACK PEN.

HOW ABOUT DECORATING THE CLOWN WITH BITS
OF PAPER CUT FROM MAGAZINES, SCRAP FABRIC, FOIL
ETC? GO FOR A CLOWN COLLAGE!

WHAT ABOUT STICKING TH
CLOWN TO THE FRONT O
A FOLDED PIECE OF
COLOURED CARD TO MA
A GREETINGS CARD?

Poster
Paint

SHELL SHOCKED!

GET CRACKING AND MAKE THIS PRETTY MOSAIC FRAME DECORATED WITH EGGSHELLS!

1 Next time mum's boiling some eggs, ask her to save the shells. Wash them and leave them to dry on some newspaper.

2 Break up the eggshells and paint them in different coloured metallic paint. Leave them to dry.

3 Make your frame by cutting two rectangles the same size from cardboard.

4 Cut a smaller rectangle from the centre of one piece of cardboard to make a frame about 6cm wide. Tape the two pieces of cardboard together on three sides with masking tape, leaving the top open to slide in your picture.

5 Draw your design onto the frame, keeping to simple, bold shapes. Paint it in flat colours and leave it to dry. Make sure you cover all the edges, too. Use base colours that match the metallic colours you have chosen.

6 Work on one area of colour at a time. Cover the whole area with a thin layer of PVA glue. Press the pieces of eggshell onto the wet PVA. This can be messy, so try to keep your fingers as clean as possible and use a cocktail stick to carefully move the eggshell into position.

7 Continue until all the frame is covered with eggshell, then leave it to dry. If any glue has discoloured the metallic paint, just touch it up when everything is in place.

NOW ALL YOU NEED IS A FAVOURITE PICTURE TO PUT IN YOUR FRAME!

FEATURES!

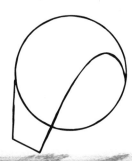

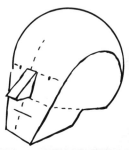

To draw a profile or three-quarters view of a head, start with a circle. Copy the pictures below to find the correct position for the eyes, nose and mouth.

The eyes are round - that's why they're called eyeballs! The lids follow the eye's rounded shape. The top lid curves more than the bottom lid.

For a three-quarters view of a nose, draw a rectangle and a triangle together and then build up the shape like this.

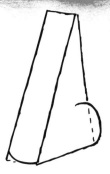

Where the lips meet in the middle, the line is curved.

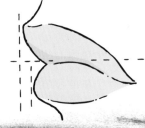

Cartoon features are even easier to draw! Try these comical expressions!

Draw a portrait from the front, starting with the basic head shape. Eyes should be about half-way down the face, the nose is in the middle and the mouth is three-quarters of the way down.

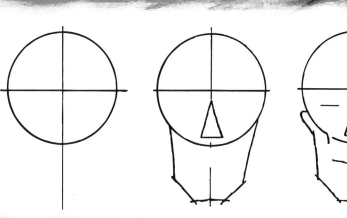

To draw eyes from the front, draw a flat lemon shape with a circle inside. Add curved lids and a smaller round pupil. Draw eyebrows and colour in the pupil.

Get the basic nose shape by lightly sketching it within a rectangle like this. Noses are slimmer at the top and wider towards the bottom. Add dark ovals for nostrils.

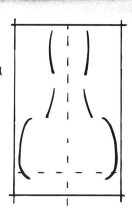  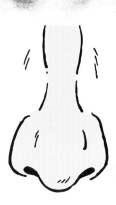

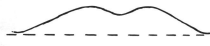 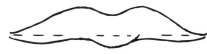 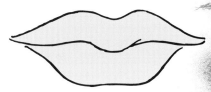

Men's lips are usually longer and narrower than women's lips. Start by drawing one lip at a time.

If you don't want to get serious, have a go at these funny features instead!

47

TEE-RRIFIC TOP!

A PLAIN WHITE T-SHIRT CAN BE TRANSFORMED WITH SOME UNIQUE PRINTS. YOU CAN USE POTATOES, FOAM, CARDBOARD OR SPONGE TO MAKE YOUR PRINTING BLOCK. COPY THESE IDEAS OR THINK UP A FEW OF YOUR OWN!

GAME ON

MAKE THE FOLLOWING SHAPES FROM POTATOES: head, arm, L-shape for leg, shirt, shorts, small rectangle for sock, boot and a round shape for the ball.

1) Protect your work surface with plenty of newspaper. Place a sheet of cardboard or a thick wad of paper inside the T-shirt so that the fabric paint does not soak through to the back.

2) Start by printing the shirt and shorts. Dip the shirt shape in red fabric paint and press on to the fabric. Print it two or more times. Then dip the shorts shape in blue fabric pant and print underneath each shirt shape.

3) Dip the head shape in skin coloured paint and print. Repeat with the arm. The L-shape can be reversed, enabling it to print both the right and left legs!

4) Print a sock shape in red at the end of each leg, and black boots. Then print a ball and you will have a football game to wear across your chest!

5) Finally, leave the paint to dry and iron the T-shirt, which will fix the paint, so it won't wash out next time your T-shirt goes in the washing machine!

You will need:

2 or 3 large potatoes, fabric paints in blue, red, skin colour, black, green, pink, cotton T-shirt, cardboard, newspapers.

PETAL POWER

Cut a simple petal shape which can also be used for leaves (just wash off one colour, then print with another!)

Print a round shape for flower centres, surround with petals, then print stems and leaves. Easy!

FABRIC PAINTS

Fabric paints are available from craft shops. You only need to buy a few basic colours to start with - red, yellow, blue and black - as other colours can be mixed. Follow the manufacturer's instructions carefully. You usually have to leave your printed fabric to dry thoroughly, then iron it with a hot iron to 'set' the colours and make them machine washable.

They work best on cotton fabrics, so make sure your T-shirt is cotton! Also make sure it has been washed before you start because the fabric paints do not work very well on new, unwashed fabric!

49

DOWN TO EARTH!

Recycle in style with this wicked waste bin! Use it to save things for making Art Attacks or collect stuff for recycling bins.

1 Cut the 4 sides and base from cardboard box card. Each side measures 32cm high with a top edge of 27cm and a base of 16cm.
Cut out a base for the bin measuring 16cm square.

27cm
32cm
16cm
16cm
16cm

2 Tape the pieces together firmly like this and then tape an upside-down paper plate to one side.

3 Cover the bin, inside and out, with at least three layers of torn newspaper pasted on with diluted PVA glue.
Leave to dry thoroughly.

PVA

4 Paint the whole thing white and then decorate any colour you wish.
Paint the plate to look like Earth and add an appropriate slogan.

Save the PLANET

save the

PLANET

ON THE BALL!

1 Cut out a large rectangle of strong cardboard. This one measures approximately 50cm x 30cm.

2 Cover it carefully with the sticky-back plastic, smoothing it flat so there are no bubbles.

3 Cut strips of white paper and stick them in position with PVA glue to mark out the pitch. Cut out a circle for the centre.

4 Copy or trace the goalkeepers printed here onto thin card, colour them in and cut them out. Tape them to the short end of some bendy straws with masking tape.

5 Paint the goals green and add white lines for the nets on both sides.

6 Use a black marker to draw the football pattern on the polystyrene ball. It must be waterproof or it will run when you blow on it.

52

Strong cardboard, green felt sticky-back plastic (from hardware stores), white paper, PVA glue, lolly sticks, thin card, paint, bendy straws, sticky tape, small styrofoam ball, waterproof black marker pen.

YOU'LL NEED TWO PLAYERS AND LOTS OF PUFF FOR THIS GAME!

VERY HANDY!

Create a hand from simple shapes, starting with a circle. There are 3 main areas: the palm, the thumb and the fingers.

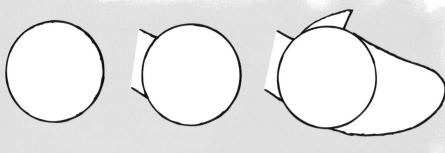

GET A GRIP!

Use 3-dimensional rectangles to get the shape correct. Actually, hands are larger than you think - practise by drawing around your own hands on to paper.

CARTOON CAPERS!

Drawing cartoon hands is easy - they don't even have to have the correct number of fingers! Use sausage and egg shapes to create some comical hands.

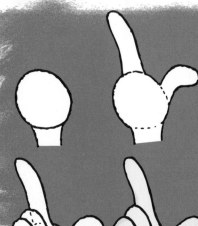

PUT YOUR FOOT IN IT!

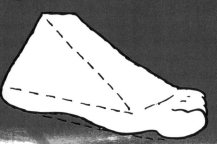

From the side, a foot is wedge-shaped with the narrow end being at the ankle.

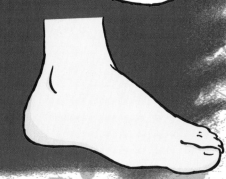

TIPPY TOES!

Use a rectangle to help you get the proportions right. Draw a slightly wiggly line inside the shape. Add toes and an ankle. Finally erase the rectangle. Get someone to model for you so you can practise!

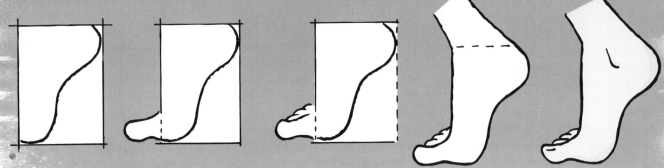

FUNNY FEET!

Try these for size! Exaggerating certain characteristics is great when cartooning. Take a look at these chunky feet!

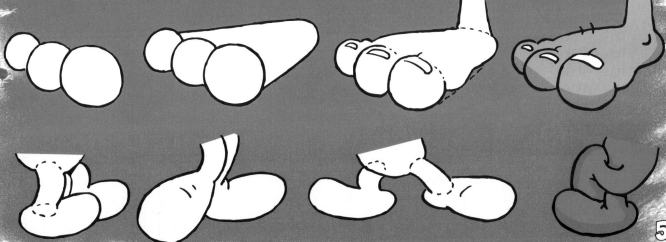

CAPTIVATING

DRESS UP AS A FAIRYTALE HERO OR HEROINE
WITH THESE AMAZING ACCESSORIES!

PRINCE CHARMING

YOU WILL NEED:
Thin gold card, tape measure, safety scissors, sticky tape, pom-poms, fabric shapes, sparkly card, tinsel, PVA glue, cardboard box card, newspaper, paints, paintbrush.

CROWN

Ask an adult to measure round your head and help you cut a piece of gold card the right size. Cut points along one of the long sides and tape the two short sides together. Decorate with glitter glue, sequins, fabric shapes and pom-poms, and finish with a length of tinsel glued around the bottom edge.

SHIELD AND SWORD

Draw a shield and sword shape onto a piece of cardboard box card and cut them out. Cut extra strips of cardboard for the cross in the middle of the shield and the sword's handle and tape them into position. Cover with two layers of papier mâché and leave them to dry. Paint as shown, then decorate with sequins.

> Make up a crest of your own by painting pictures of things you're interested in, such as your favourite sport, or something to do with your home town.

COSTUMES!

PRETTY PRINCESS

YOU WILL NEED:
Thin gold card, tape measure, safety scissors, sticky tape, pom-poms, fabric shapes, sparkly card, tinsel, PVA glue, cardboard box card, newspaper, paints, paintbrush.

CROWN

Follow the instructions for making the Prince's crown, but instead of gluing tinsel around the bottom edge stick some glittery pipe cleaners to the top at the front as shown.

PENDANT

Cut a circle of gold card and decorate it with a fabric star, glitter glue and sequins. Wrap a glittery pipe cleaner around the edge, then stick a length of sparkly thread on so you can hang it round your neck.

RING

Cut a thin band of gold card big enough to wrap around one of your fingers and tape it closed. Cut a small heart from gold card and cover it with glue, then sprinkle it with glitter. When it's dry, decorate the heart with sequins.

OCEAN VIEW!

AHOY THERE, SHIPMATES! WHAT'S THROUGH THE PORTHOLE TODAY? SLIDE SOME FUN PAINTINGS INTO THIS FANTASTIC PORTHOLE FRAME AND CHANGE YOUR VIEW OF THE WORLD!

1 Draw around a large dinner plate onto the cardboard and cut out two circles.

2 Place a smaller bowl or plate in the centre of one circle of card and draw around it. Cut out the inner circle to create a frame about 6cm wide.

3 Glue small balls of kitchen paper around the frame at regular intervals to look like bolts.

4 Cover the frame and the outside edge of the backing circle with a thin layer of kitchen paper, using PVA glue diluted with water. Leave it to dry.

58

5

Paint the frame and the edge of the back piece and leave them to dry.

PAINT SOME SEA-THEMED PICTURES ONTO CIRCLES OF THIN CARD. TRY A STORMY SEA, A TREASURE ISLAND, A PIRATE SHIP, A LIGHTHOUSE, A MERMAID ON A ROCK, A CORAL REEF OR EVEN A SEA MONSTER!

6

Glue the front part of the frame to the back, making sure you only put glue half way around the circle as shown. Leave the top half open so you can slot in different pictures. When it's dry, pop your picture into place and you'll be all at sea!

How to Draw LIGHT & FORM!

If there is a light source, objects have shadows. The pictures below show the effect of a moving light source on solid shapes. Can you see how the shadows seem to make the objects look more solid?

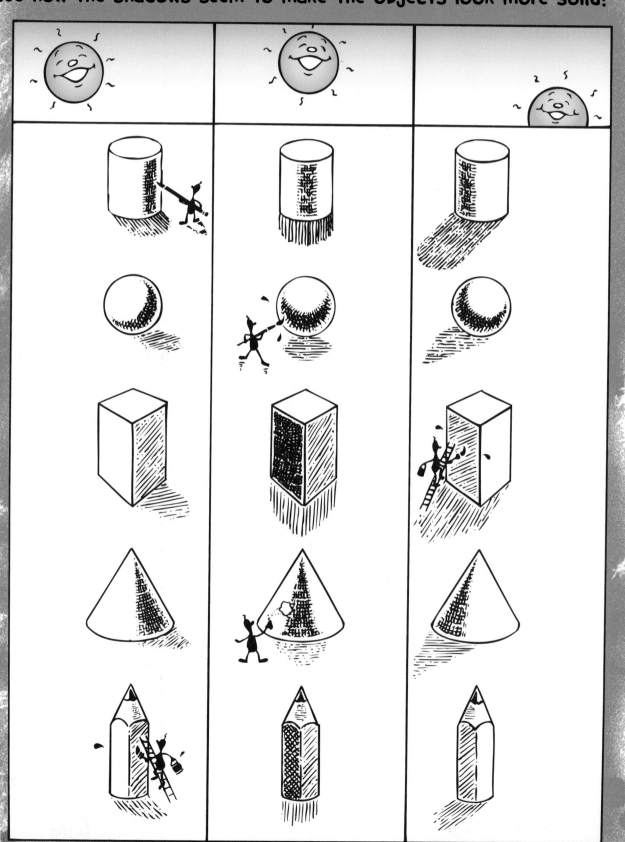

TASTY TREATS

Adding shading (form) to common objects using a strong, single light source makes objects appear more solid.

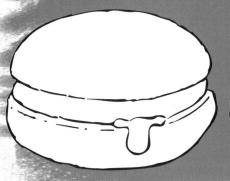

PEAR-SHAPED!

This pear goes from looking flat and plain to a rounded, more realistic looking pear.

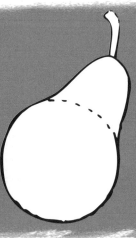

FIZZY FUN!

The shadows on this can help to make it look shiny and three-dimensional. Apply shadow to the curved areas of the can to create this illusion.

RUGGED RUCKSACK!

See how this technique creates texture on fabric as well?

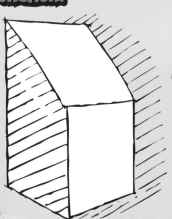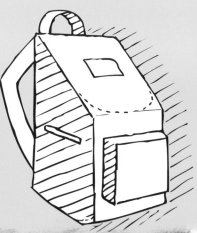